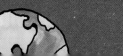

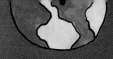

Welcome to this World

A Love Letter to Little Ones

By **Debby Boone** / Illustrated by *Gabriel Ferrer*

HARVEST HOUSE
PUBLISHERS
Eugene, Oregon 97402

Copyright © 1995 by Resi, Inc.
Published by Harvest House Publishers
Eugene, Oregon 97402

Library of Congress Cataloging-in-Publication Data
Boone, Debby.
    Welcome to this world / Debby Boone : illustrated by Gabriel Ferrer.
        p.   cm.
    Summary : Describes in illustrations and simple text some of the
wonders waiting to be discovered by a new baby.
    ISBN 1-56507-302-9
    [1. Babies—Fiction.]   I. Ferrer . Gabriel, ill.   II. Title.
    [E]—dc20   95-30155
                                                          CIP
                                                           AC

Quote on page 32 taken from *The Bible, The Supernatural, and the Jews*
by McCandlish Phillips (© 1970, reprinted 1995 by Horizon House Publishers,
Camp Hill, PA), p. 380. Used with permission.

Printed in Mexico

97 98 99 00 01 02 - 10 9 8 7 6 5 4 3 2

Dearest Little One,
Welcome to this world—

A world that
has become
more wonderful...
just because
you're here!

And just like you, the world is full of gifts to be discovered and enjoyed...

Like the
sunrise
that
celebrates
the gift
of each
new day

Or the morning dew that glistens with hope on a springtime meadow.

And as the
wildflowers
drink their fill

You can
almost hear
them laughing.

When you see
the first green
sprout of your
summer garden
start to push
through the
warm, dark earth,

Know that in life there is always something to look forward to.

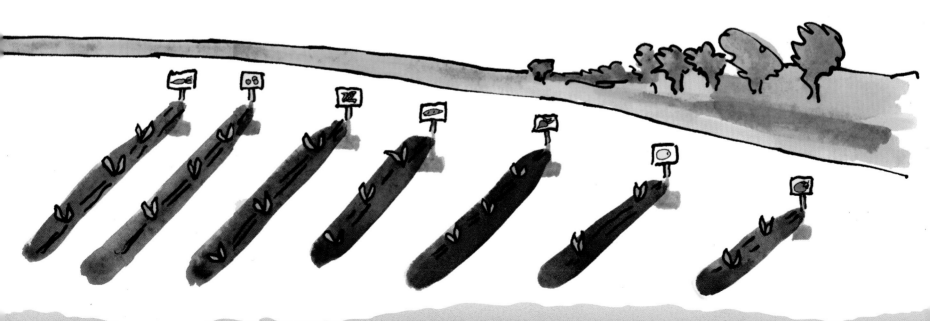

And just as the sunflower (which grows taller than you are on your father's shou(lders) lifts its face as if to kiss the sun

Don't ever forget how much
there is to be thankful for.

Enjoy the curiosity that makes you see for yourself that no two snowflakes are alike.

You'll find your fingerprint is like that—no one else's is exactly like yours.

But if you look in the mirror, you might see your father's eyes, or your mother's smile,

And you'll be a little closer to finding out what makes you...you.

I can't wait for you to have your first little puppy.

You'll love him so much it will almost hurt...and he will love you back.

That's how
I love you.

There will be so much for you to do
and see. Climbing mountains can
give you a great new point of view.

It's good to stop—and notice—
the wonder all around you...

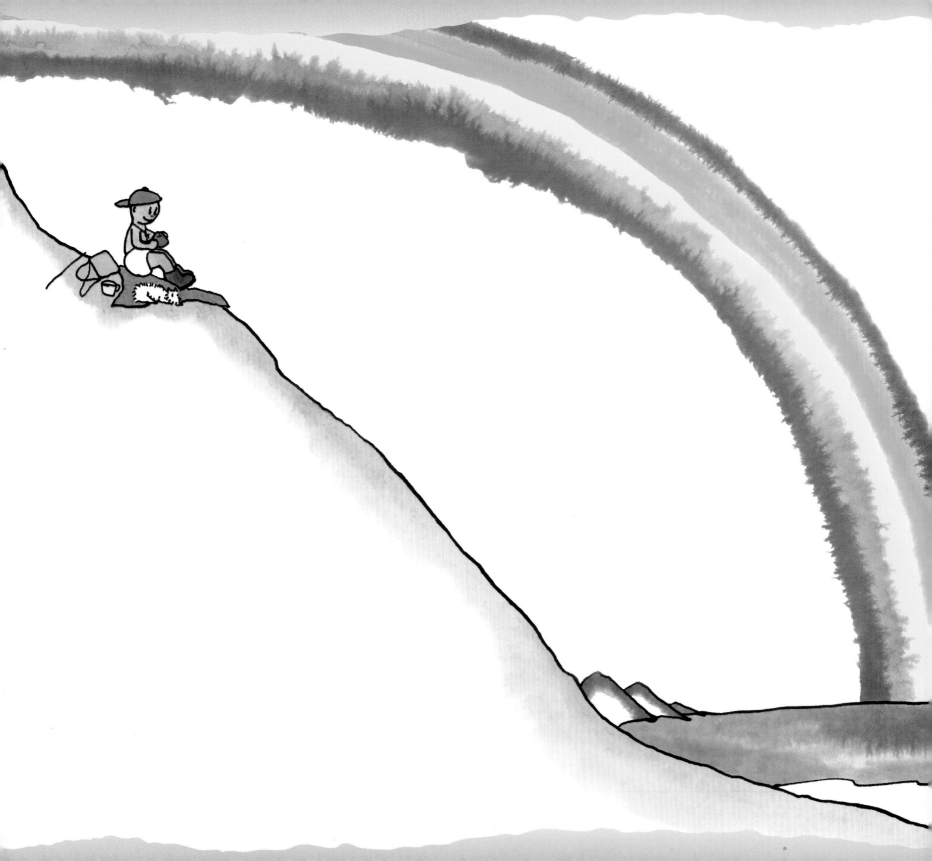

Like when golden sunbeams
brighten the darkest sky,

And suddenly a rainbow
stretches from heaven to
earth like a dream come true,

Or the beach at sunset that has the stillness of a painting though there is movement all around you.

The wind
is like a
symphony...

Waves rush
to the shore
like beautiful
ballerinas all
in a row,

Each one dancing for joy.

Every night the moon and
the stars continue the dance,

And sometimes you'll feel
they're very close,

Welcome to this world!

If you have never heard the
mountains singing, or seen the trees
of the field clapping their hands,
do not think because of that that
they don't. Ask God to open your
ears so you may hear it, and your
eyes so you may see it, because,
though few men ever know it,
they do, my friend, they do.

McCandlish Phillips